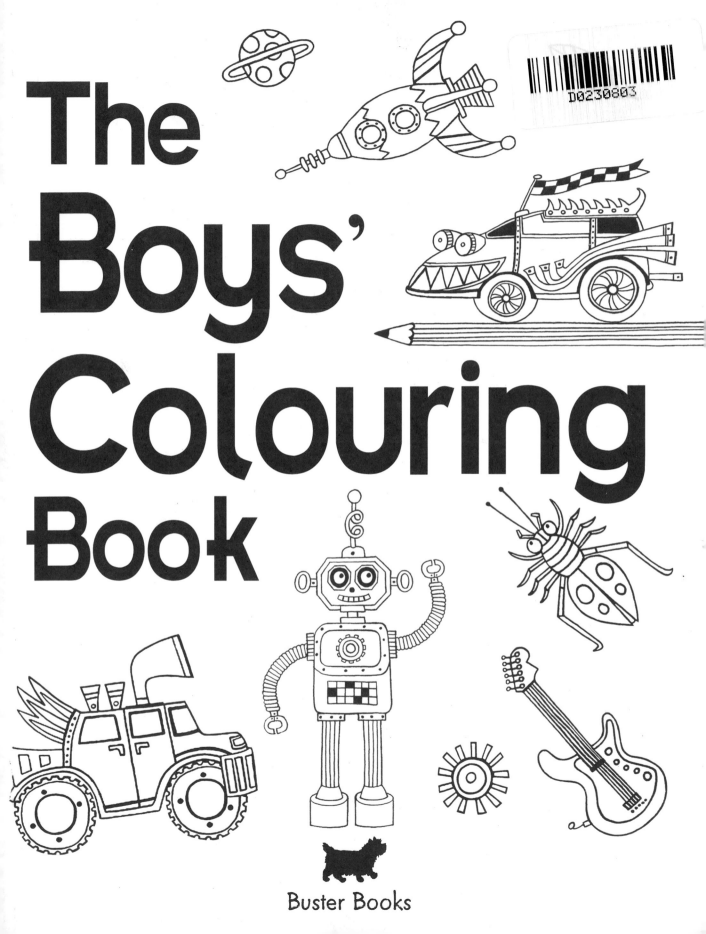

The Boys' Colouring Book

Buster Books

Illustrated by Jessie Eckel

Cover design by Angie Allison

First published in Great Britain in 2009 by Buster Books,
an imprint of Michael O'Mara Books Limited,
9 Lion Yard, Tremadoc Road,
London SW4 7NQ

With thanks to Becky, Adam and Dylan

A CIP catalogue record for this book is available from the British Library.

ISBN: 978-1-906082-89-5

6 8 10 9 7 5

www.mombooks.com/busterbooks

This book was printed in February 2011
at WKT Co. Ltd., Shenzhen, Guangdong, China.

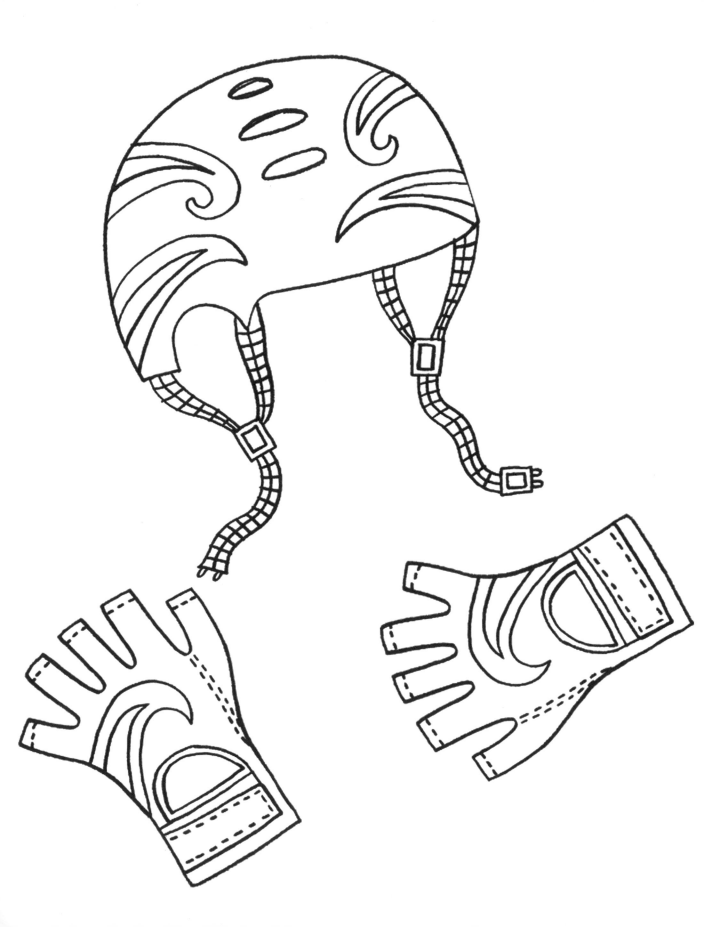

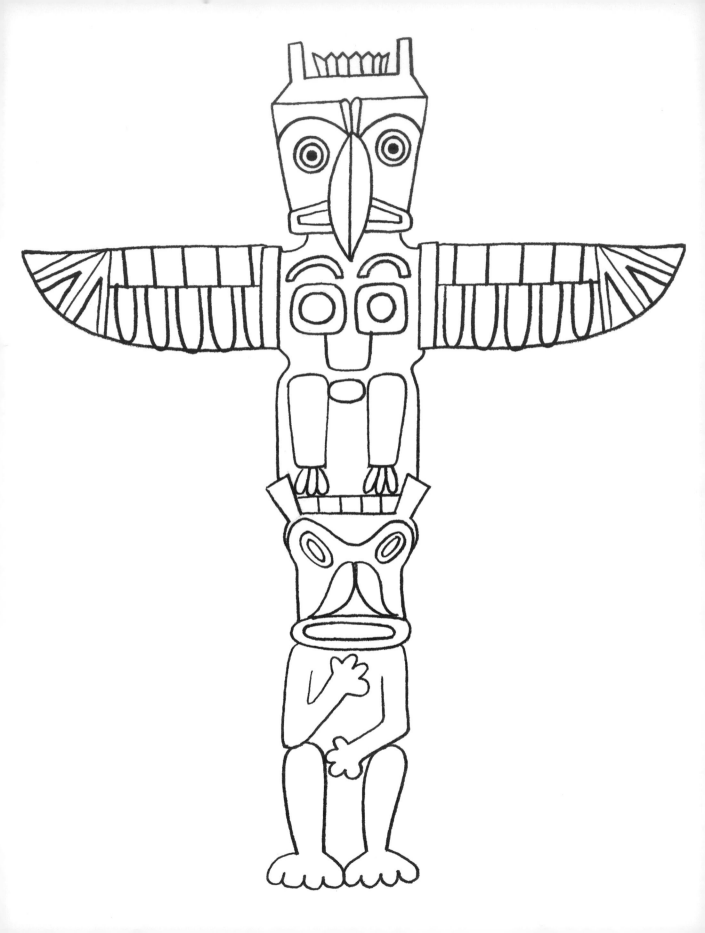

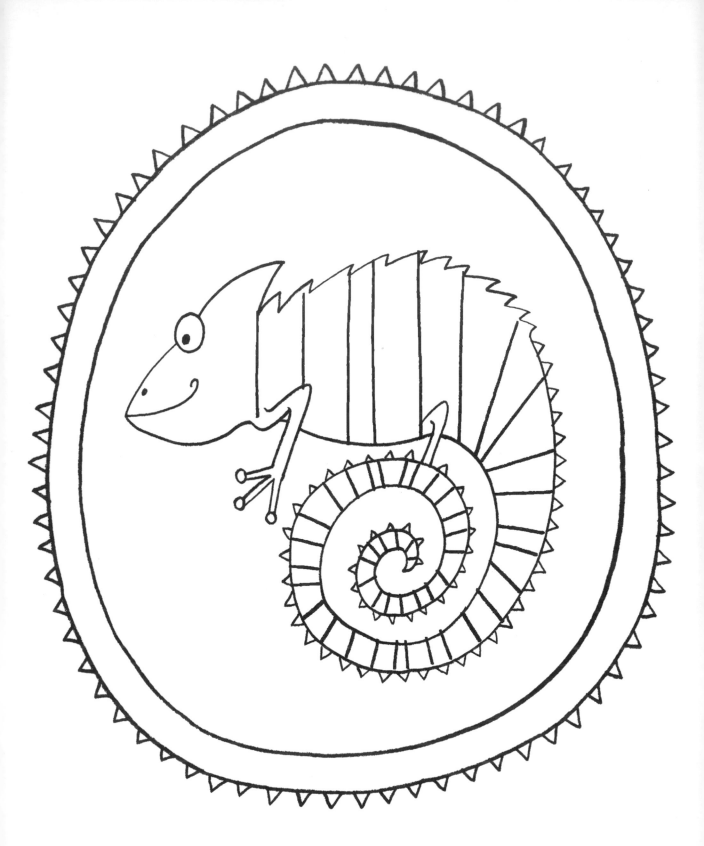

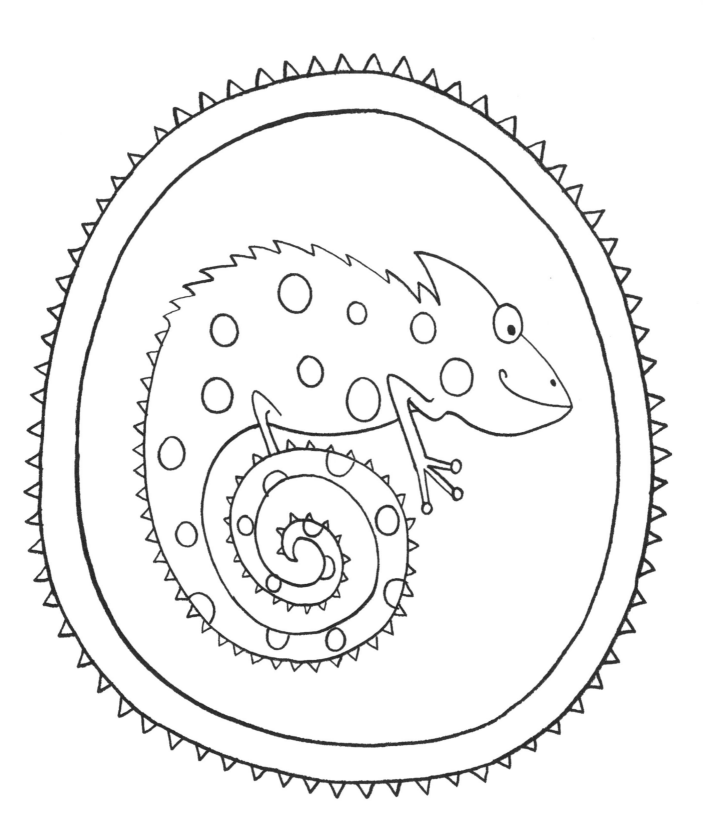

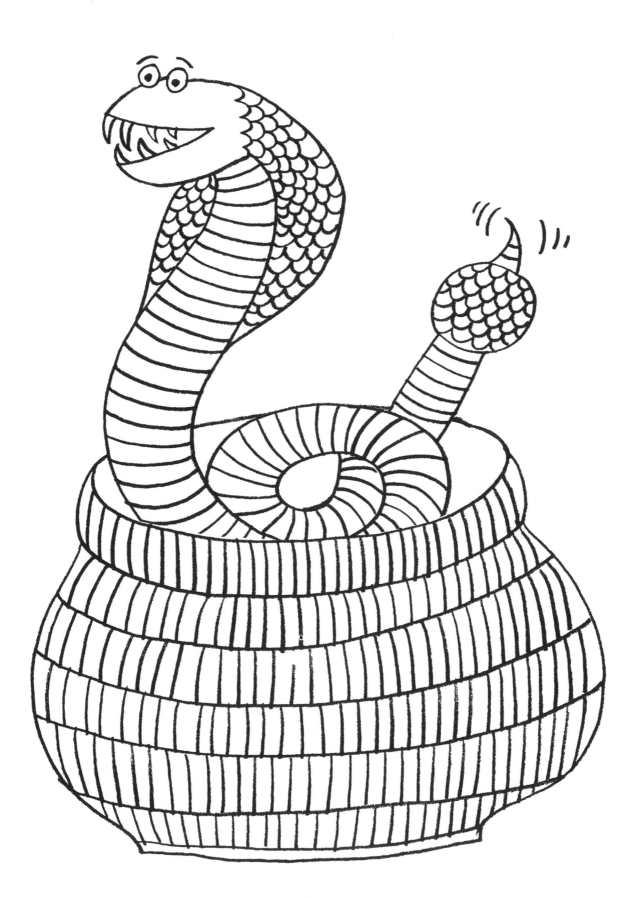

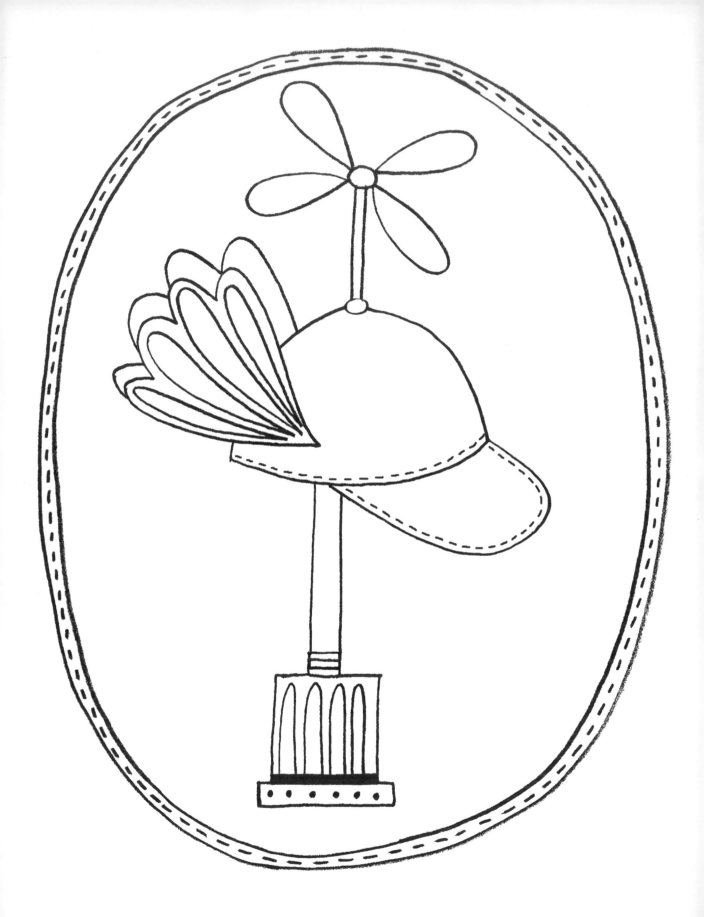

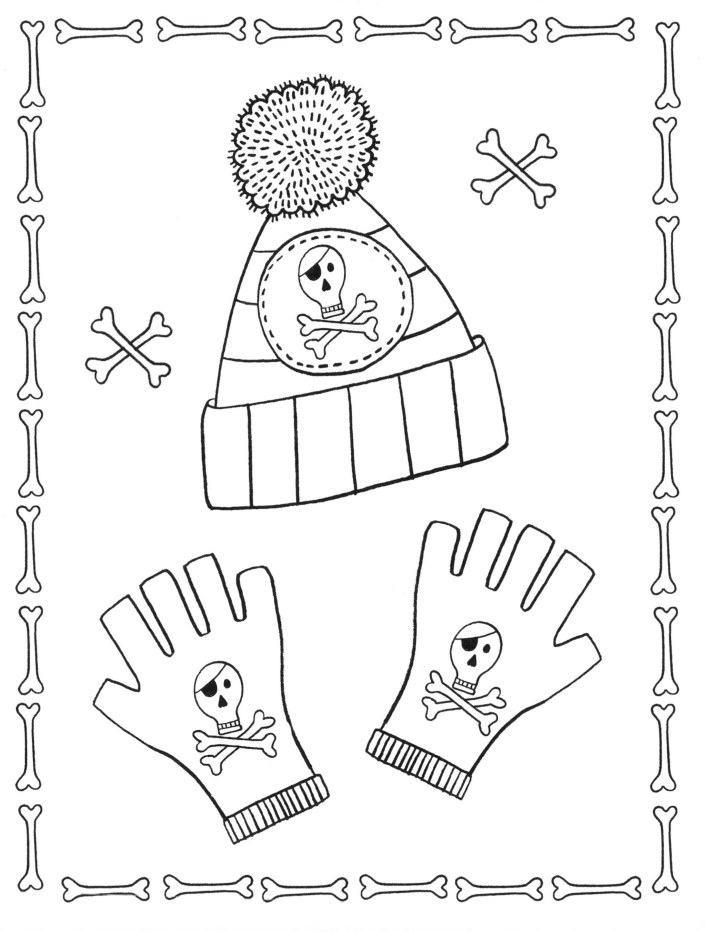

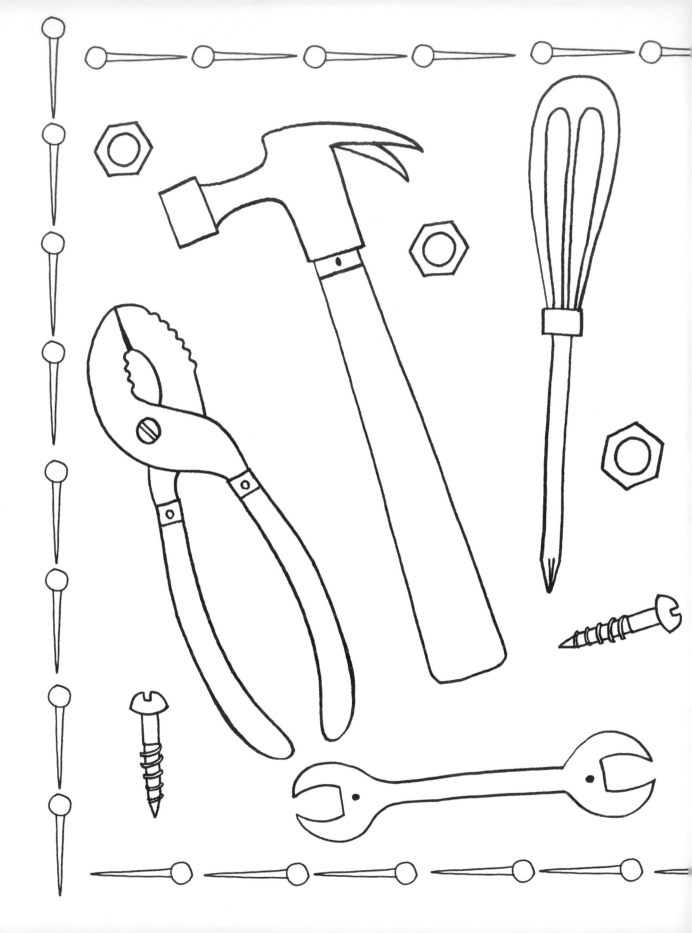

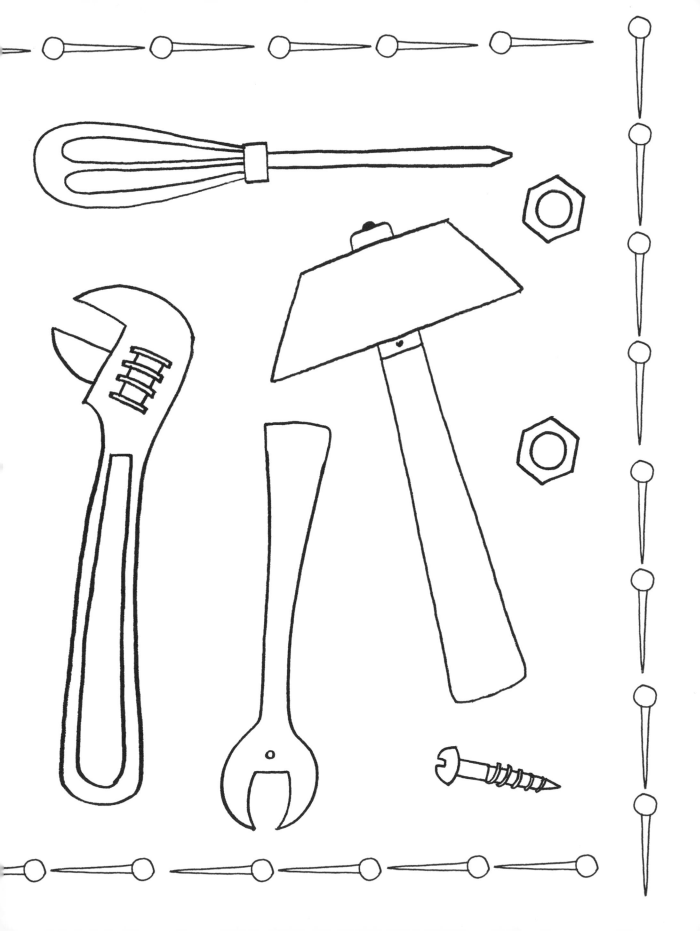

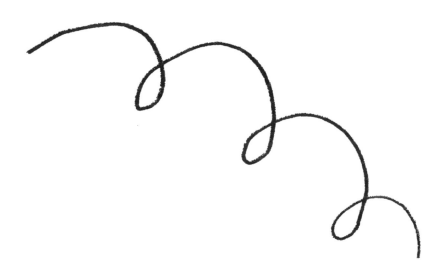

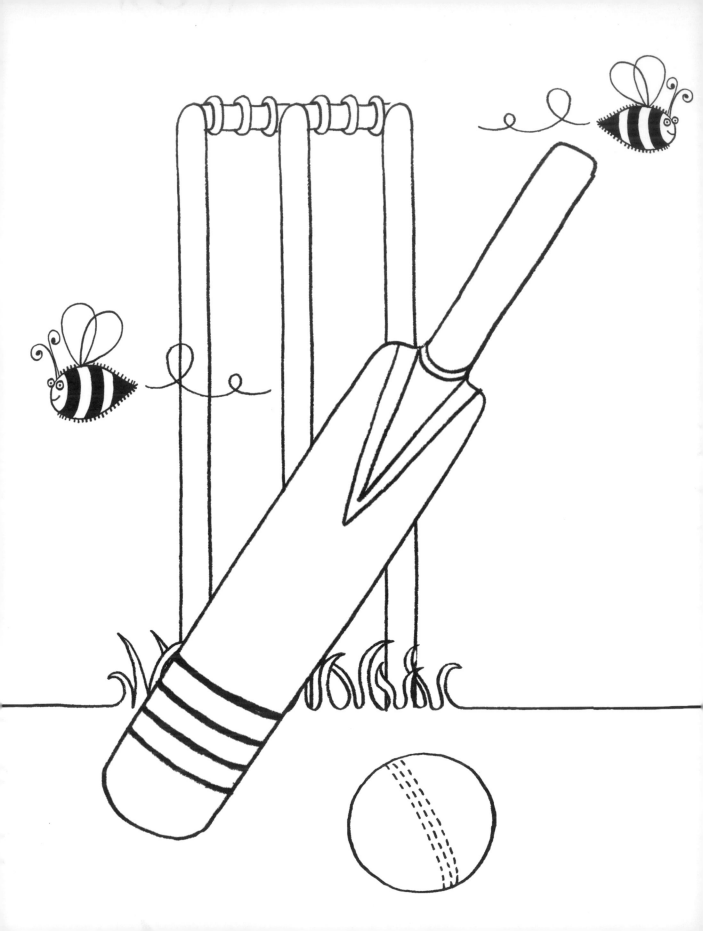

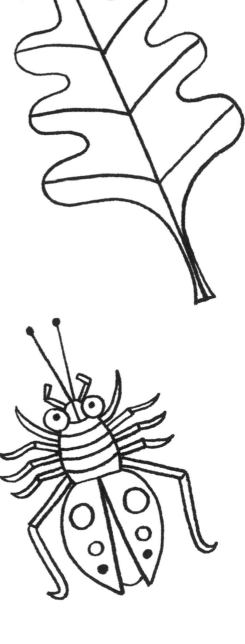

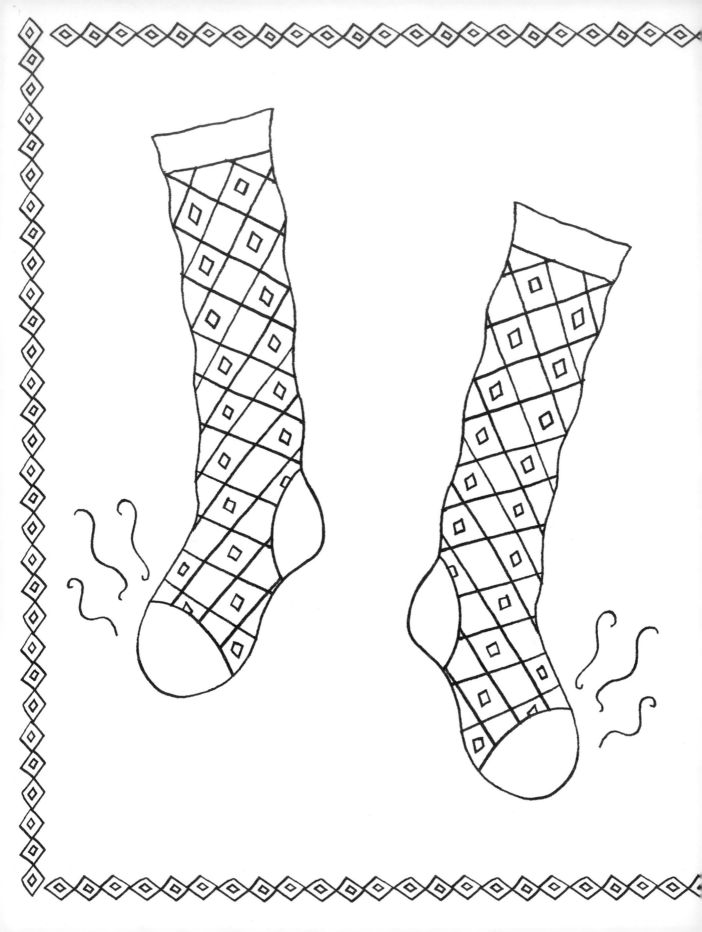

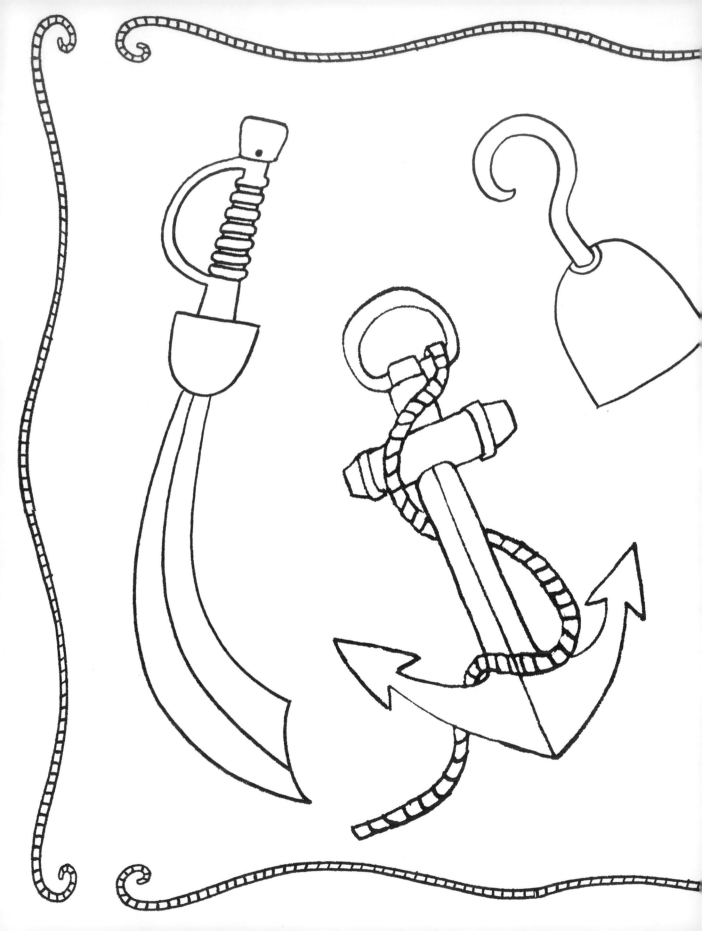

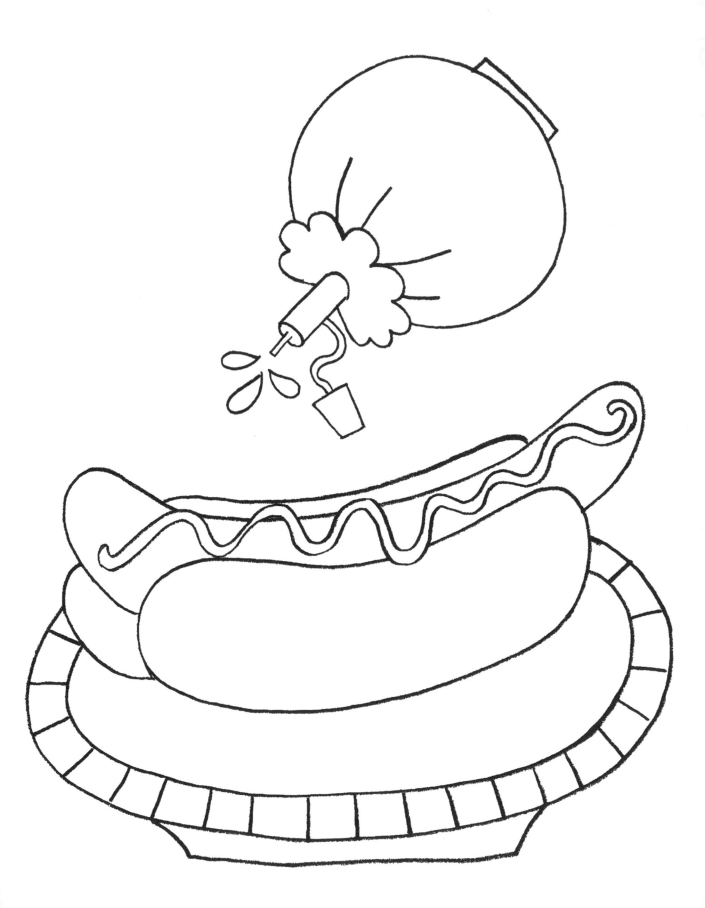

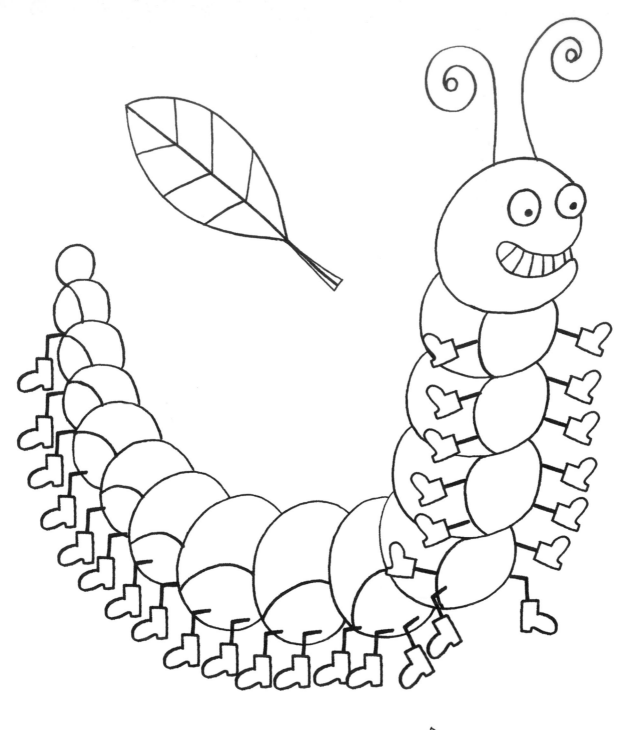
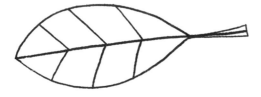
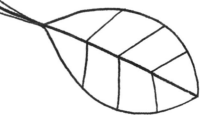

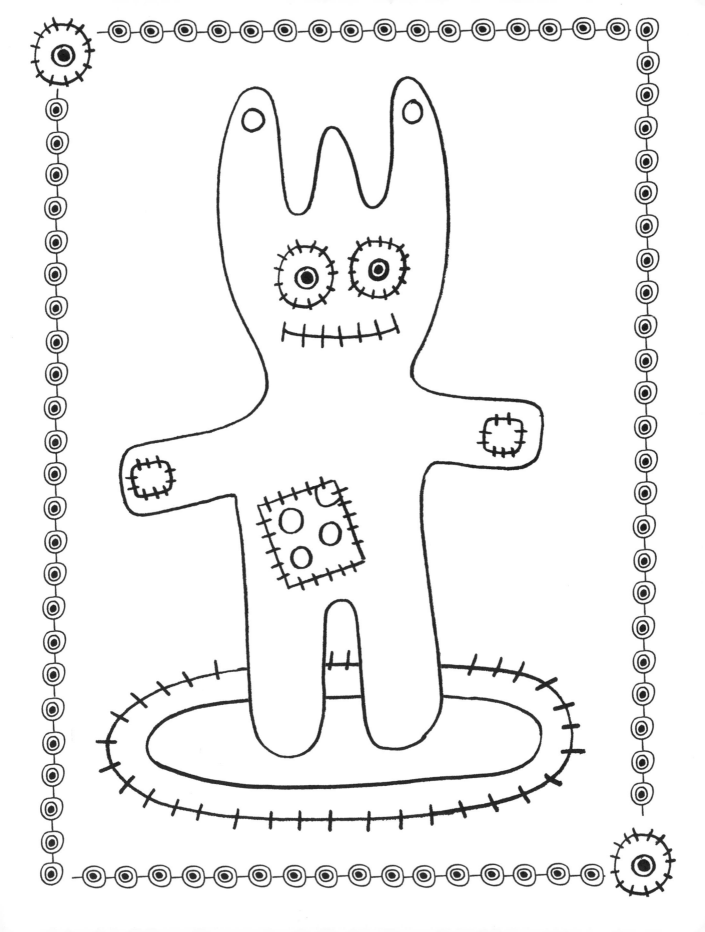

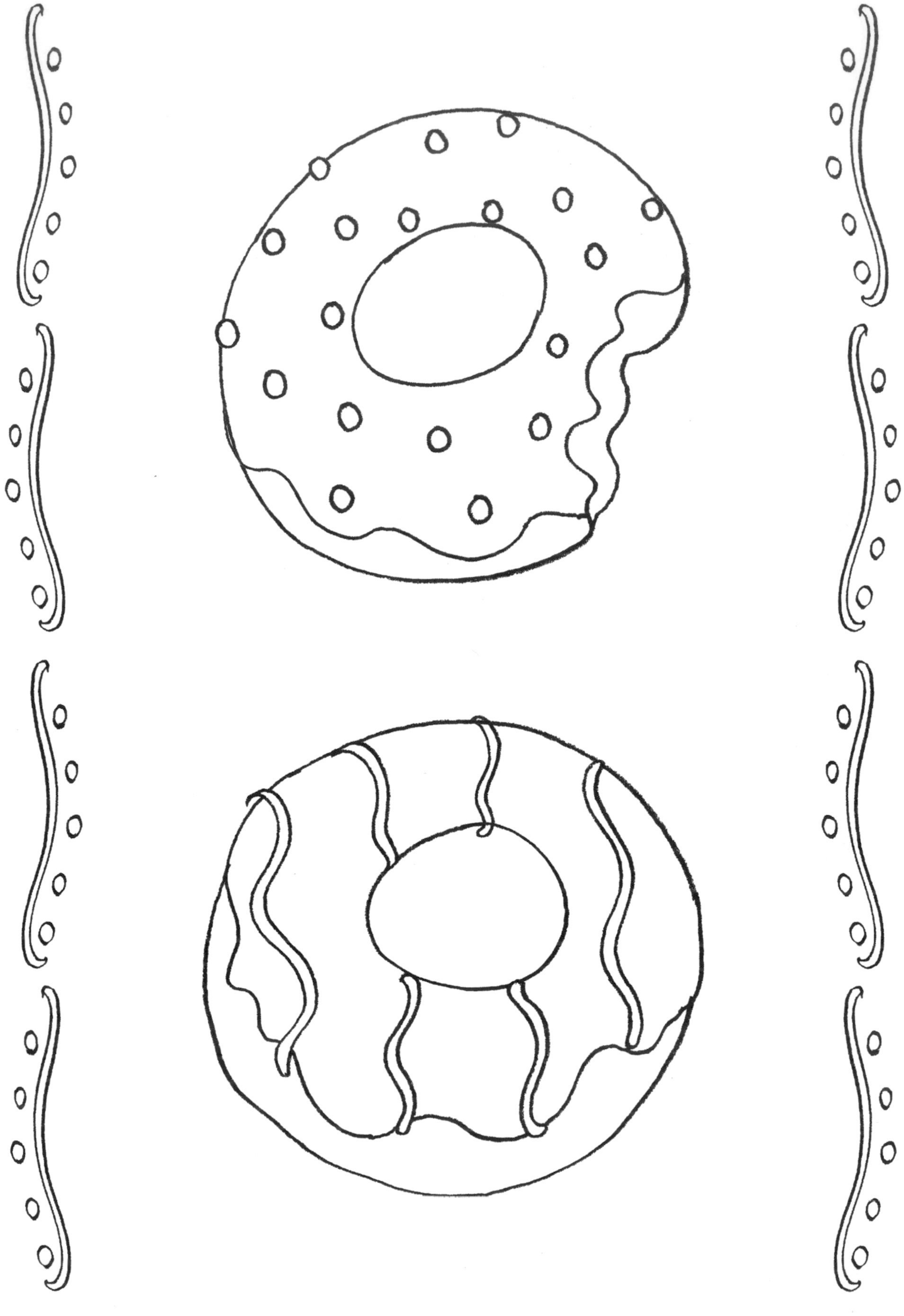

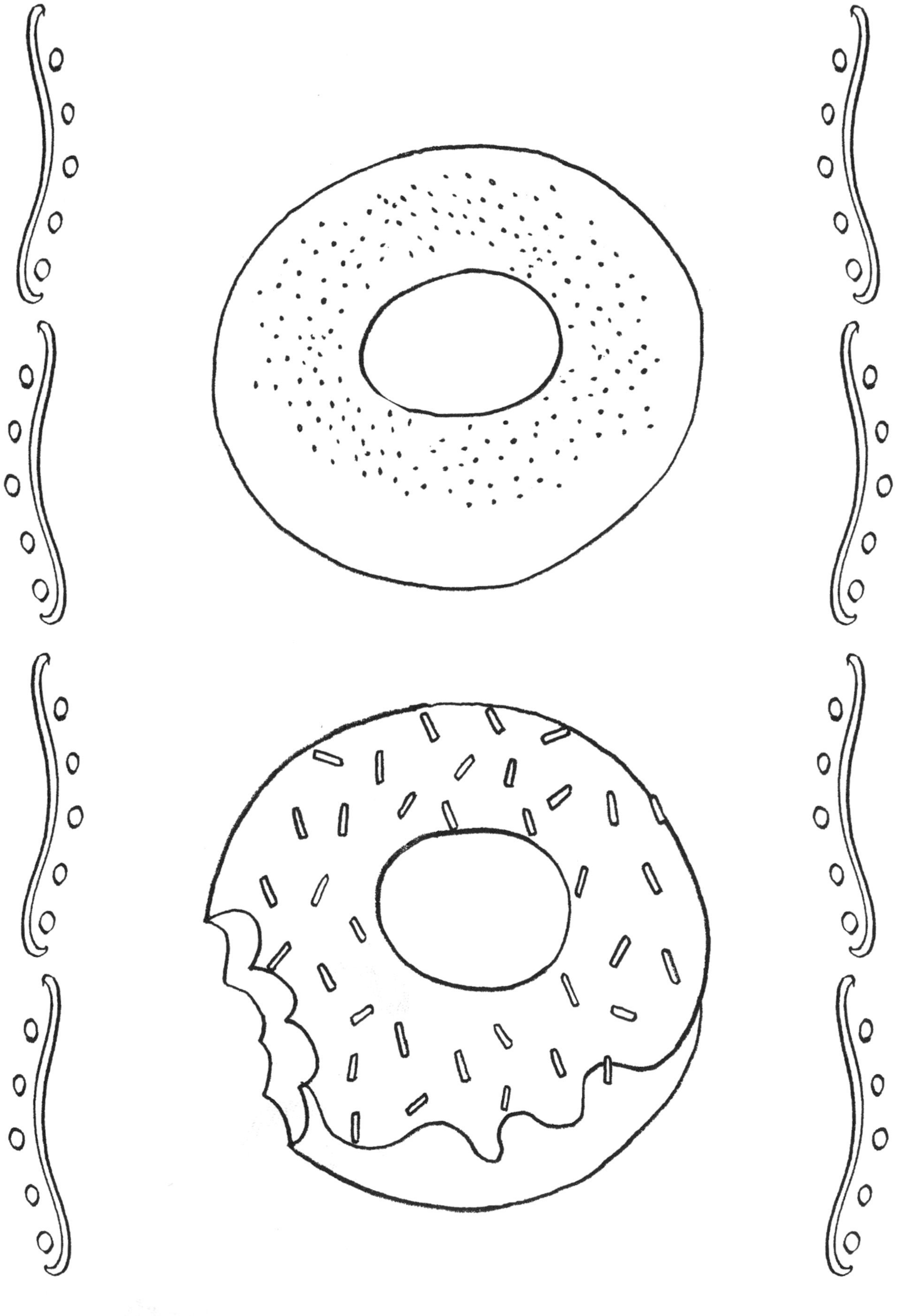